HPS 1136

LEONARD BERNSTEIN

SERENADE

after Plato's "SYMPOSIUM"

for Solo Violin, Strings, Harp and Percussion

LEONARD
BERNSTEIN
*Music Publishing
Company LLC*

BOOSEY & HAWKES

AN IMAGEM COMPANY

DISTRIBUTED BY

HAL•LEONARD®
CORPORATION
7777 W. BLUEMOUND RD. P.O. BOX 13819 MILWAUKEE, WI 53213

Commissioned by the Koussevitzky Foundation

First performed September 12, 1954
at Teatro La Fenice in Venice, Italy,
by violinist Isaac Stern and the Israel Philharmonic Orchestra
conducted by the composer

RECORDINGS

Isaac Stern and the Symphony of the Air
conducted by the composer: CBS ML/CML 5144, Odyssey 343633

Zino Francescatti and the New York Philharmonic
conducted by the composer: CBS MS 7058, CBS 72643 (U.K.)

Serge Blanc and the Orchestre Philharmonique de l'ORTF
conducted by Georges Tzipine: SB 001 France

Gidon Kremer and the Israel Philharmonic Orchestra
conducted by the composer: Deutsche Grammophon 2531 196

PROGRAM NOTE

On August 8, 1954, the day after completing his score, the composer wrote the following description of its origin:

There is no literal program for this *Serenade,* despite the fact that it resulted from a re-reading of Plato's charming dialogue, "The Symposium." The music, like the dialogue, is a series of related statements in praise of love, and generally follows the Platonic form through the succession of speakers at the banquet. The 'relatedness' of the movements does not depend on common thematic material, but rather on a system whereby each movement evolves out of elements in the preceding one.

For the benefit of those interested in literary allusion, I might suggest the following points as guideposts:

I. *Phaedrus; Pausanias* (Lento; Allegro). Phaedrus opens the symposium with a lyrical oration in praise of Eros, the god of love. (Fugato, begun by the solo violin.) Pausanias continues by describing the duality of lover and beloved. This is expressed in a classical sonata-allegro, based on the material of the opening fugato.

II. *Aristophanes* (Allegretto). Aristophanes does not play the role of clown in this dialogue, but instead that of the bedtime story-teller, invoking the fairy-tale mythology of love.

III. *Erixymathus* (Presto). The physician speaks of bodily harmony as a scientific model for the workings of love-patterns. This is an extremely short fugato scherzo, born of a blend of mystery and humor.

IV. *Agathon* (Adagio). Perhaps the most moving speech of the dialogue, Agathon's panegyric embraces all aspects of love's powers, charms and functions. This movement is a simple three-part song.

V. *Socrates; Alcibiades* (Molto tenuto; Allegro molto vivace). Socrates describes his visit to the seer Diotima, quoting her speech on the demonology of love. This is a slow introduction of greater weight than any of the preceding movements; and serves as a highly developed reprise of the middle section of the *Agathon* movement, thus suggesting a hidden sonata-form. The famous interruption by Alcibiades and his band of drunken revellers ushers in the Allegro, which is an extended Rondo ranging in spirit from agitation through jig-like dance music to joyful celebration. If there is a hint of jazz in the celebration, I hope it will not be taken as anachronistic Greek party-music, but rather the natural expression of a contemporary American composer imbued with the spirit of that timeless dinner party.

INSTRUMENTATION

Violin I
Violin II
Viola
Violoncello
Contrabass
Harp
Timpani
Percussion (five players):
    Snare Drum
    Tenor Drum
    Bass Drum
    Triangle
    Suspended Cymbal
    Tambourine
    Chinese Blocks
    Xylophone
    Glockenspiel
    Chimes

Duration: *ca.* 30 minutes

This work is also published in a transcription by
the composer for violin and piano (SAB-105)

Materials for orchestral performance are available
from the Boosey & Hawkes Rental Library

SERENADE
after Plato's "SYMPOSIUM"

I Phaedrus: Pausanias

Leonard Bernstein
(1954)

N. B. The solo violin part edited and fingered by Isaac Stern.

5

6

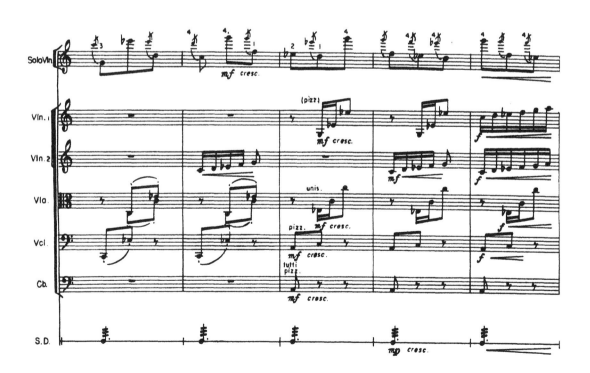

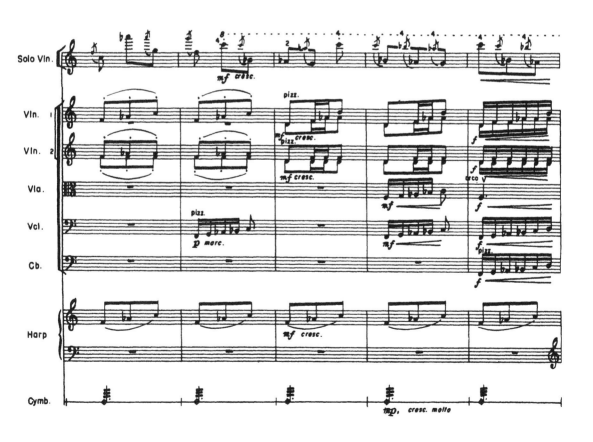

22

Con fuoco

II Aristophanes

F

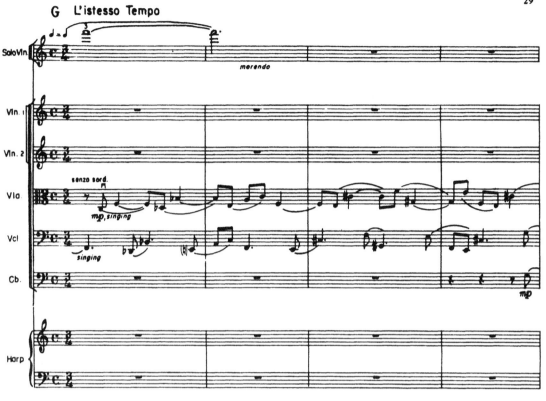

H

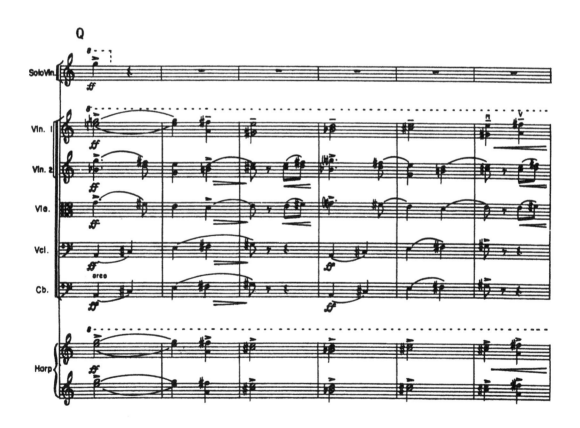

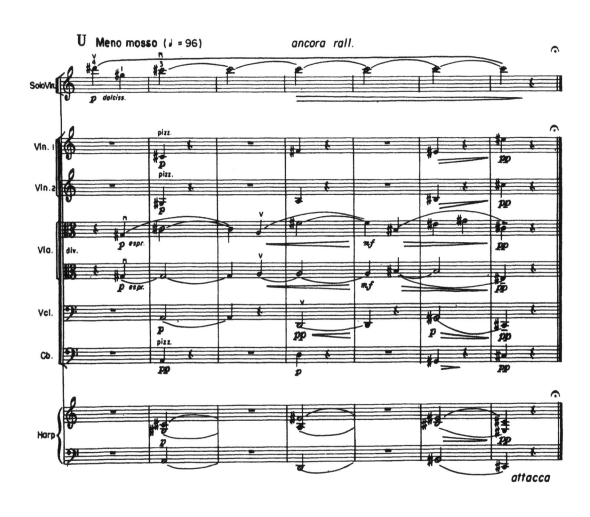

III Eryximachus

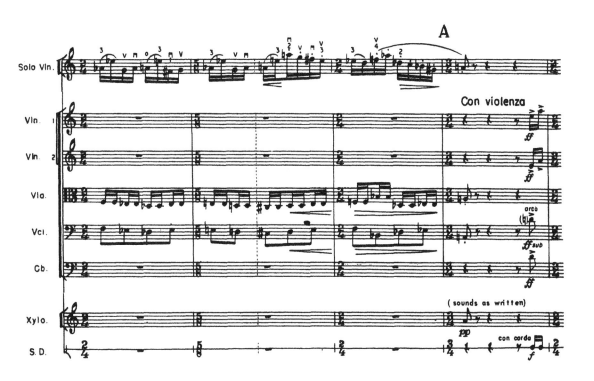

Vln. 1
Vln. 2
Vla.
Vcl.
Cb.
S. D.

* If possible, it is preferable that all notes be played Tutti

Solo Vln.
Vln. 1
Vln. 2
Vla.
Vcl.
Cb.
Timp.
S. D.

ª It is preferable that all 6 violins play all the notes, if possible.

* It is preferable that all notes be played tutti, if possible

* Tutti play all notes, if possible

* Play all notes if possible

IV Agathon

F

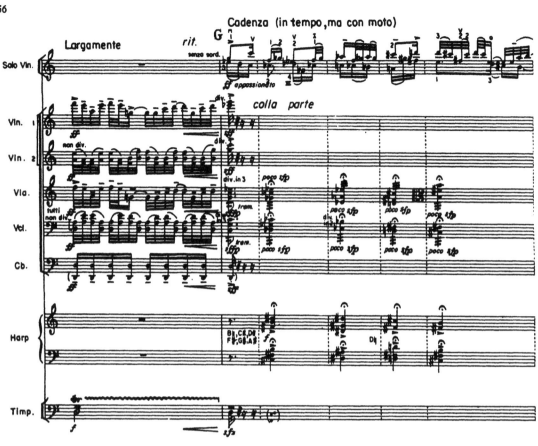

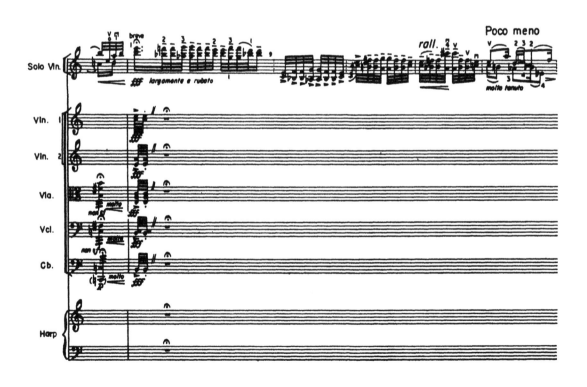

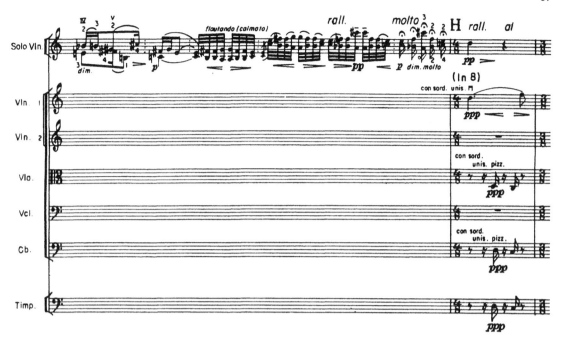

I Poco meno

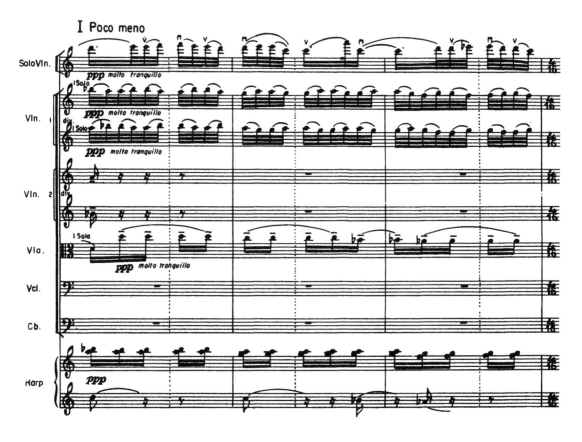

V Socrates: Alcibiades

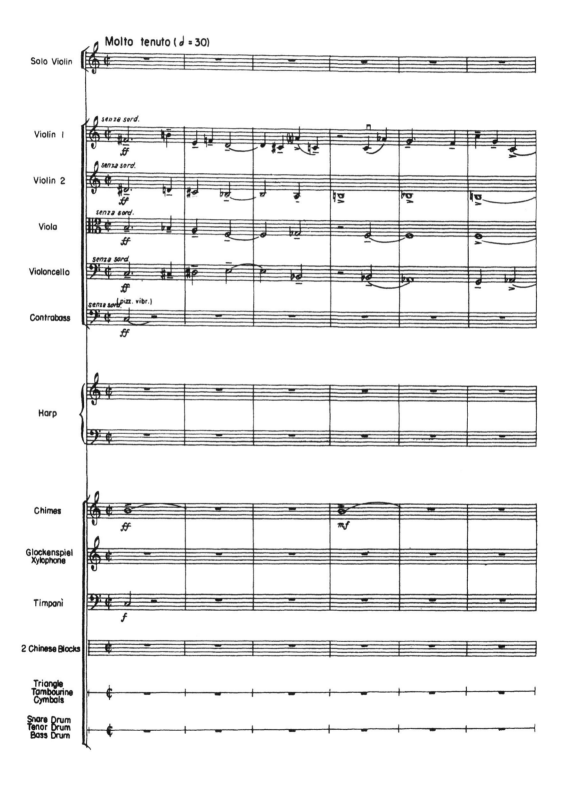

1

poco rit.   Meno mosso (in 4) (♩ = 54)   *avanti*

2

Più mosso (♩ = 92)   poco string.

3

Subito meno, come sopra (♩ = 54)

* Attention is called to the key signatures of two flats in the Solo Violin, and two sharps in the Solo Cello.

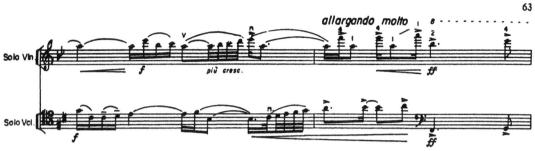

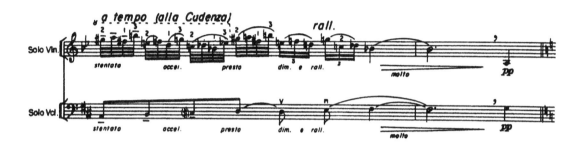

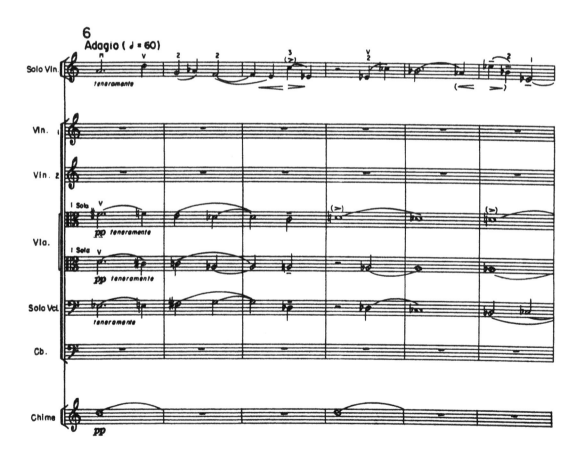

8

Allegro molto vivace (♩. = 132)

19

23

34

Molto giocoso

43909

A tempo, molto giocoso

Vineyard Haven,
August 1954